Books are for everyone
but this book belongs to:

Cindy Henze 314 So, 13th ST, ST Charles

Illinois.

Pioneers of the Church

by Grace Storms Tower
Illustrated by Roger Martin

UNITED CHURCH PRESS
BOSTON · PHILADELPHIA

Library of Congress Catalog Card Number 64-19471

This book is part of the United Church Curriculum, prepared and published by the Division of Christian Education and the Division of Publication of the United Church Board for Homeland Ministries.

CONTENTS

About This Book 1

DEMETRIUS OF ANTIOCH 3

CARL OF WITTENBERG 27

JOHN ELIOT, *Apostle to the Indians*............41

FRONTIER PREACHER 63

TORNADO IN TOWN 75

Pronouncing Names 91

ABOUT THIS BOOK

HERE is a collection of stories about very different people who have one thing in common. They all are "church pioneers."

In the first story you will meet Demetrius of Antioch who is angry with the church. His god is Apollo, who is worshiped with games and feasting. Demetrius' family is Christian, and Demetrius cannot understand why, for Christians do not seem to have any fun. Then Demetrius meets an unusual person who helps him to understand—and to want to be a Christian himself.

The second story takes place fifteen hundred years after Demetrius. Eleven-year-old Carl meets a man whose ideas about the church throw the whole world into an uproar. Carl wonders for a long time whether the man is right or wrong, but finally he makes up his mind.

In the third story a minister has a conviction about the church that takes him on a visit to a warring Indian chief and leads him to translate the Bible into a new and difficult language. The fourth story is about a man who changes his church membership, goes into hiding, and becomes a great American frontier preacher.

The final story is about some junior boys and girls who discover that belonging to the church brings some hard problems. They almost make a wrong decision. But just in time they remember what the church is. See if you think they, too, may be church pioneers.

DEMETRIUS OF ANTIOCH

CHRISTIAN! Christian! Run away, Christian!" The mocking cry echoed in the streets of Antioch.

Nicholas stepped to the doorway of his shop and looked out, but he could not see the people who were shouting. For a moment he stood there, wondering what had happened to provoke the taunts. He was just turning back to his work when he heard another voice. "I'm not! You know I'm not. Go pick on someone else!" That voice belonged to Demetrius, his son.

Demetrius was out of breath and angry as he burst through the shop door, almost knocking his father over.

"They chased me all the way here," he panted. "I wasn't doing anything, just walking along the street like everyone else. Why do they call *me* 'Christian'?"

"I'm sorry, son," Nicholas answered. "Those people who were making fun of you probably know that I'm a follower of Jesus Christ. They think you are too. They've taken to calling all of us 'Christians.'"

"Well, I'm not a follower, and I don't like to be called names. If there hadn't been so many of them, they would have been sorry."

"Demetrius, I know it isn't fun to be laughed at. It hurts. But we won't stop this name-calling by fighting back. Now let's try to forget it for a little while. There's work to do."

Demetrius was still breathing hard as he followed his father to the rear of the shop. His fists were clenched and his jaw firmly set. "It

3

isn't fair," he muttered under his breath. "If I ever get a chance, I'll show them!"

Nicholas heard the words, but he did not say anything. Instead, he went over to a new shipment of goods that had arrived the evening before.

"We must get these things ready to sell," he directed. "And I think there's something here you'll want to see."

"What is it?" Demetrius asked without much interest.

"When you come to it, you'll know," Nicholas replied.

Demetrius' curiosity was aroused, and he started to ask another question. But remembering what had just happened to him, he shrugged his shoulders. He was not going to let anything make him forget how he felt.

Without even looking at his father, Demetrius set to work, carefully placing the lengths of silk and brocade on one low table and the copper and silver bowls on another. In spite of himself, he looked for the article his father had mentioned.

Everything he picked up was beautiful, for his father sold only the finest merchandise in his shop. Finally, almost everything was in order. Only a small ivory box remained. Demetrius picked it up and started to place it on a low shelf.

"Look inside," his father suggested.

Demetrius obeyed, and gasped at what he saw. In the box, resting on a dark blue silk cushion, was the most beautiful gold necklace he had ever seen.

"What are you going to do with it?" Demetrius asked.

"It was a special order for a family whose daughter is to be married next month," Nicholas answered. "It's the finest workmanship I've ever seen. I want your mother and sister to see it too."

"But Eunice won't want you to sell it! I'll bet she'll want to keep it for herself," Demetrius declared.

Nicholas shook his head. "Your sister will like it," he agreed. "But she will not care about having it."

4

Demetrius touched the necklace. The gold was delicately shaped into a chain of small flowers, each of which caught the light of the sun that came in through the door of the shop.

"Eunice will want it," Demetrius insisted. "None of her friends have a necklace like this!"

"No, they don't," Nicholas agreed. "But you forget that the followers of Jesus don't wear such jewelry, and Eunice is going to be baptized very soon. This means more to her than any jewelry."

Demetrius started to say something, then stopped. He knew he must not argue with his father. But the memory of the taunting cry of "Christian" came back to him. Why did his family have to be different? Why couldn't they wear fine clothing and eat rich food, and enjoy the games and festivals just as the other families in Antioch did? He turned away from his father and went back to the rear of the shop.

Nicholas watched his son. He guessed what Demetrius was thinking. "Someday," Nicholas said to himself, "I hope Demetrius will understand why we are followers of Jesus. But I can't *make* him understand."

In the late afternoon, Demetrius helped his father close up the shop. There would be no selling tomorrow, for it would be the first day of the week, the Lord's Day. When everything was in place, Nicholas picked up the ivory box, and together he and Demetrius started toward their home on the slope of the hill behind the city.

News!

Demetrius liked being outdoors at this time of day when the western sun shone on the marble buildings and down the broad avenue that crossed the center of the city. The people who hurried along the streets seemed as gay as the sparkling fountains and the bright flowers in the courtyards of the homes.

Soon his own home came into view, a low building of stone with a number of rooms constructed around an open courtyard. In the courtyard there were flowers and a small fountain.

5

As Demetrius and his father came nearer, they were surprised to see Eunice standing in the doorway, looking down the street.

"I wonder if something is wrong," Nicholas said. "I hope your mother is all right."

He and Demetrius walked more rapidly. "Eunice doesn't look upset," Demetrius replied as they drew closer. "She looks as if she were excited about something!"

A moment later Eunice saw them and came hurrying in their direction. "We have news," she called. "Exciting news!"

"What is it?" Demetrius asked. "Has something happened?"

"No," Eunice answered. "But it will soon. Mother learned about it from Jason. She's waiting to tell you."

At the mention of Jason, Demetrius lost interest. Jason was a leader in the group of followers of Jesus. "Whatever the news is, it doesn't concern me," Demetrius thought.

His father felt differently. When he heard his daughter's words, he hurried into the house.

Inside it was dim and cool. For a moment neither Demetrius nor his father could see clearly. Then, as his eyes became accustomed to the change in light, the boy saw his mother coming toward them from the courtyard.

"What have you heard, Helen?" Nicholas asked.

"Paul and Barnabas are coming—here to Antioch, and soon!" she replied. "Jason learned it this morning from one of our group who passed them on the road from Jerusalem. They will be here in just a few days."

"This is great news!" Nicholas exclaimed. "It has been a long time since they were in Antioch."

"Jason also said that Paul has a plan he wants to talk over with us, but Jason has no idea what it is. We'll have to wait until Paul himself tells us. But now you must be hungry and tired."

Helen set out the food for the evening meal. After the family had sung a psalm, they bowed their heads while Nicholas prayed, "O eternal

6

God, who has made thyself known to us in Jesus Christ, bless this food we are about to eat and keep us faithful to thee. Amen."

During the meal, while his mother, father, and sister talked excitedly about the coming of Paul and Barnabas, Demetrius said very little. He tried hard not to show how he felt. On their first visit to Antioch, Paul and Barnabas had made followers of his family—"Christians!" How Demetrius disliked that word. Because his parents were followers of Jesus, they thought it was wrong to do all the things Demetrius enjoyed, and right to do things he wasn't at all sure he liked.

He looked at the food on the low table before him. Because of Paul and Barnabas he was eating milk and cheese and this dark bread instead of the rich foods and pastries he liked so well. Because of Paul and Barnabas he was laughed at by the other boys. His sister and mother no longer wore beautiful clothing and jewelry. Now Paul and Barnabas would be here again, perhaps staying in his own home. There was no telling what would happen this time!

After the meal, the family walked out into the courtyard. It was cool and pleasant in the early evening. Overhead a bright, full moon dimmed the stars. Demetrius looked out across the city and breathed deeply. One thing had not changed—Antioch.

For a few moments he stared at the river that reflected the light of the moon and the dark slopes of the hills rising above the town. His eyes traveled toward the west. There in the forest of laurel and cypress trees was the great temple of the god Apollo. At one time his family had worshiped this god, and he could remember the fun he had had attending the festival of Apollo each summer. In those days his mother and father danced, ate, and sang. Now there were no feasts and dancing. Now the only excitement was over the visit of two men—two Christians! Why did everything have to change?

Demetrius followed the others into the house and went to bed, his mind still filled with questions to which he could find no answers. And because there was no one he could turn to for help, he felt very much alone.

I Don't Want to Be a Christian

Long before dawn Demetrius was awakened by his sister. "It's time to get up," she called. "I think you'd sleep right through the day if we let you!"

"What's there to get up for?" he started to ask, and then changed his mind. There was no use starting an argument. Still half asleep he slipped into his clothes and joined the others, who were ready to leave for the Lord's Day worship.

They hurried along the quiet streets. As they entered the large house where the followers of Jesus Christ gathered to worship, the first rays of the sun spread across the eastern sky. Inside, Demetrius went with his mother and sister to one side of the room, while his father went with the men to the other. The group became silent, waiting for the words of the leader that would announce the beginning of the service.

Demetrius looked at the people who were present. Everyone seemed happy and expectant, as though something wonderful were about to happen. Was he the only one, he wondered, who felt out of place, as if he didn't belong?

The voice of the leader broke into his thoughts.

> "Great and wonderful are thy deeds,
> O Lord God the Almighty!
> Just and true are thy ways,
> O King of the ages!"

"Amen," the group responded.

The service went on. The leader read a passage from the prophets and then a psalm. The air of quietness and expectancy continued. Each person listened as though this were the first time he had heard these words.

Then the leader announced the coming visit of Paul and Barnabas. Paul would probably lead the service on the next Lord's Day. In spite of himself, Demetrius began to share some of the excitement, but his mood changed quickly as his mother touched his arm. It was time for him and his sister to leave the service.

The two of them joined the others who had not yet been baptized and went to another room in the house where they could wait until the service was over.

"I don't see why we can't stay," Demetrius complained to Eunice. "What do they do that's so secret?"

Eunice looked at her brother in surprise. "We haven't been baptized," she reminded him. "This part of the service is only for those who know that they are followers, those who can be trusted to serve Jesus no matter what happens."

"Well, I don't like it," he responded.

"We'll be baptized before long," she said. "Then we can stay."

"I don't think I want to be baptized," Demetrius burst out. "I don't like being called 'Christian' and I don't like having all the people in Antioch laugh at me!"

"Demetrius!" Eunice exclaimed. "What a thing to say! Does Father know about this?"

"I guess he does," Demetrius answered more quietly. "But Mother doesn't, and don't you say anything. I'll tell them sometime."

Eunice looked troubled. "All right, I won't," she promised. "But I hope you change your mind."

"Well, I won't; you can be sure of that," Demetrius told her. "And I'm through talking about it."

Eunice shrugged her shoulders and went over to sit with a group of girls. Demetrius was left alone, deep in his own unhappy thoughts.

When the service was over, Nicholas and Helen joined their children. It was still early morning as they walked toward home, but now Antioch was awake. Most of the shops were open for business, for only the Christian storekeepers closed on Sunday. Boats moved up and down the river, and the streets were crowded with hurrying people.

"This evening some of us are meeting to plan for the coming of Paul and Barnabas," Nicholas told his family as they entered the house.

"Can they stay with us while they're here?" Helen asked her husband.

"I hope Paul can," Nicholas replied. "There are many who will want them in their homes, and I don't know how much time they can spend in Antioch."

Demetrius frowned but said nothing. Suddenly he noticed the carved ivory box that his father had brought home the evening before and then forgotten in the excitement.

"Father!" Demetrius exclaimed. "You didn't show Eunice and Mother the gold necklace!"

Nicholas laughed. "No, I didn't. The news about Paul and Barnabas drove it from my mind. If your mother and sister want to see it, you may show it to them."

Demetrius did not wait to be urged. He brought the small box over to them and opened the lid with a flourish. There lay the necklace. The sunlight touched the fragile gold flowers and made them shine.

Eunice gasped with delight. "May I touch it?" she asked.

"Yes," her father answered. "You may hold it if you wish."

Eunice lifted the necklace gently. It was more beautiful than anything she had ever seen.

"Wouldn't you like to wear it?" Demetrius asked.

Eunice carefully laid the necklace back in the box. "Yes, I really would," she answered.

"But you never will," Demetrius said. "Followers of Jesus don't wear expensive jewelry, or eat good food, or do a lot of things everyone else can do."

"Demetrius!" his mother exclaimed. "What are you saying?"

Eunice glared at her brother. "He doesn't want to be baptized," she said. "He doesn't want to be called 'Christian' and be laughed at. He told me so this morning."

Demetrius looked angrily at his sister. "You promised you wouldn't say anything!"

"I don't care," she declared. "Mother and Father should know. You should have told them yourself and not pretended to be something you aren't."

"Eunice! Demetrius!" Nicholas scolded. "I want to know what has been going on here. Now, what did you say, Demetrius?"

Demetrius looked defiantly at his sister, but when he tried to face his father and mother he found he couldn't. He wished he were miles away.

"Demetrius, I want to know what you told Eunice," his father demanded.

The boy tried to speak, but he could not. He bit his tongue as he searched for words that would not come.

"He said—" Eunice began.

"Let your brother speak for himself," Nicholas told her. Then less sternly, he said, "I know you were upset about that episode yesterday, Demetrius, so I didn't take what you said then very seriously, but now I want to know everything that has been going on. Take your time, but tell us what you told Eunice."

12

"Father—" For a moment Demetrius was afraid he would cry. "Father, I don't want to be a follower of Jesus. I want to go to the Apollo festival and the games, and I don't want to be laughed at."

Nicholas and Helen looked at each other.

"Son," Nicholas put his hand on Demetrius' shoulder, "Apollo isn't a real god. He's only a stone statue, and it's wrong to worship a statue. The true God is the God we love and serve. He means more to us than all the games and festivals of Apollo. You don't believe this?"

"No, I don't," Demetrius replied, again close to tears. "All I know is that I've lost all my friends. I wish you'd never heard of this God!"

Nicholas sighed. "I'm sorry you feel as you do. Your mother and I wish you could share the joy we have found through Jesus Christ. Someday perhaps you will."

Demetrius regarded his father in surprise. He had expected him to be angry.

For a moment there was silence in the room. Then Nicholas picked up the ivory box. "We'd better put this away so it won't be lost. Let's have something to eat. Then we can walk down to the river before I go to the meeting."

Guests and Questions

During the next few days the followers of Jesus waited impatiently for the arrival of Paul and Barnabas. Even Demetrius found himself looking hopefully at every Jewish stranger he met in the streets of Antioch.

Demetrius wasn't sure he would recognize Paul and Barnabas if he did see them. But there were moments when he wondered what he would do if he were the first to learn of their arrival. Would he tell his father? Would he run through the city shouting the news of their coming in the same way that great news from Rome was sometimes announced?

This was a decision Demetrius did not have to make, for one evening just as he and his family were finishing dinner, Jason came to report that the travelers had been seen a short distance south of the city. "They should arrive in an hour or so," he said. "And I have other news—there are three men in the party. Who do you suppose has come with Paul?"

"I don't know," Nicholas answered. He walked over to the door and looked down the street. Helen and Eunice joined him.

Jason smiled. "Watching won't get them here any faster," he remarked. "They'll be brought directly to your home by the men who have gone to meet them. They may be very tired."

"And hungry," Helen added. "We'll be ready for them."

Eunice and Helen set to work preparing more food, while Jason and Nicholas went to meet the guests. Left alone, Demetrius wandered into the garden. The night was cool and pleasant. He walked along the path for a while kicking pebbles as he went; then he sat down on a stone bench and chewed a blade of grass.

"I wonder what Paul and Barnabas are like," he said to himself. "I wish I could remember." Demetrius tried to reach back in his memory to the time when his family had first met Paul. "Just as well I can't remember," he thought. "I'll find out what they're like soon enough."

The minutes passed. Demetrius stretched out on the bench, flat on his back, watching the stars. Suddenly he heard voices from the street. "Paul and Barnabas and the mystery man have arrived!" he exclaimed. "Now what am I supposed to do?"

He answered his own question by walking toward the house. As he entered a rear door he saw three strangers standing with his father. One was tall. Demetrius decided that he must be Barnabas, and the one who was talking must be Paul. "That other one doesn't look very old," he thought.

As Demetrius drew closer, his father saw him. "Come over here, Demetrius," he said. "I want you to meet our guests."

Demetrius walked toward his father. "This is my son," Nicholas said to the men. "You saw him when you were here before, but he has grown since then. Demetrius, here are Paul and Barnabas, and with them is John Mark."

"I'm glad you arrived safely," Demetrius said politely.

The men smiled. "Thank you," Paul answered. "We're glad we're here. And I'm glad I'll be here in your home. I hope I'll see much more of you."

Demetrius bowed and stepped back. He knew it was time for him to leave so the men could talk, but he wanted to listen to Paul. "He looks as though he could do anything he wanted to," Demetrius thought as he went toward the door. "I'd like to know where he's been and what he's seen. I'll bet he knows some good stories!"

Paul turned to Jason and Nicholas. "Now," he said, "I want to know all that has been happening here in Antioch. How are the followers? Has the fellowship grown?"

The sound of voices continued into the night. Demetrius fell asleep

long before Paul lay down to rest and Barnabas and John Mark left for the homes where they were to stay. When Demetrius awoke the next morning, Paul had already gone to meet with some of the men. Somewhat to his surprise, Demetrius was disappointed. He realized that he had hoped to see Paul.

During the days that followed, Demetrius was busy. For hours at a time he was alone in the shop while his father met with Paul, Barnabas, John Mark, and the other Christians of Antioch. In the evening, groups of people gathered in Demetrius' home. Sometimes his father would close the doors and windows of the room where they were meeting, and Demetrius could not hear what Paul and the others were saying. This made him angry. But sometimes he was allowed to sit quietly in a corner of the room and listen as Paul spoke and answered questions.

One evening Paul talked about his own life. He told how he had persecuted the followers of Jesus in Jerusalem and had put many of them in prison. He spoke sadly of the death of Stephen. Then he described how his whole life had been changed by Jesus Christ.

Demetrius listened in amazement. He had not realized that Paul had once hated the followers of Jesus and had punished them for their beliefs. Demetrius thought about this, and the harder he thought the more puzzled he became. Why had Paul become a follower? What was so important and special about Jesus Christ?

One morning, so early that the sun had not yet appeared in the eastern sky, Demetrius was awakened by the sound of singing. He sat up and listened. It was a whole group of people, Demetrius could tell, and they were singing a psalm of praise. He got up and peeked into the room from which the sound came. The people who had come the evening before were still there! The meeting had gone on all night.

When the singing stopped, Paul began to pray. "The grace of the Lord Jesus Christ, the love of God, and the fellowship of the Holy Spirit be with you all. Amen."

After a moment of silence the people rose to leave. Demetrius watched his father as he talked to Barnabas while Paul spoke to some of the others. "What has happened?" Demetrius wondered. Everyone, and especially his father, seemed excited. Why had the group met throughout the night? Was something important going on? Demetrius waited with increasing impatience while the people said their farewells and went out into the empty streets.

At last Paul and Nicholas were alone. As Demetrius watched them, wondering whether he dared speak, his mother came into the room.

"Good morning, Demetrius." She looked tired but happy. "Did we wake you with our singing?"

Demetrius nodded. "I wondered who was here." He turned to his father who was smiling at him. "Why were the people still here? Is something wrong?"

Nicholas shook his head. "No, son, nothing is wrong, but we've made an important decision. We'll tell you about it later. Now we are tired."

Demetrius was disappointed. He wanted to hear the news now. Paul watched the boy closely. "Let's tell him now," he said to Nicholas. Then turning back to Demetrius, Paul said, "During the night we were thinking and praying about the needs of people in the lands to the north and west of Antioch. As we prayed, we became certain that the good news of Jesus Christ must be taken to these people. Barnabas, John Mark, and I have been chosen to carry it."

Demetrius did not understand what was exciting about this. He waited for Paul to say more.

Noticing his son's perplexity, Nicholas explained, "By the people to the north and west, we don't mean those who are within a few days' journey of Antioch. We mean the people who live across the Great Sea, in Cyprus and Greece. They have never heard of Jesus Christ and of God's great love. Paul and Barnabas and John Mark are going to these people. It will be a long and possibly very dangerous trip. We have set a day for prayer and fasting when all the followers of Jesus in Antioch will gather to send them on their way and wish them success in their labor."

"You're leaving?" Demetrius asked Paul. "Will you come back?"

"We hope to return," Paul answered. "But whatever the outcome of our travel, I know it is God's will that we go. I've thought about this for a long time, and I'm glad the followers in Antioch join me in my wish to bring to others the news of what God has done for us through Jesus Christ."

Demetrius was not sure what Paul meant. He stood, looking from one person to another, sensing that something important was happening, but puzzled about the meaning of it. Why had people stayed awake all night just to send Paul and the others away again? Why couldn't they just *go* to Cyprus and Greece if they wanted to?

No one explained, and Demetrius left for the shop, still wondering about the all-night session and the coming trip of Paul and Barnabas and John Mark.

Demetrius Learns Some Answers

On the morning that Paul was to leave Antioch, Demetrius was up early. He went quietly into the garden behind his home and sat on a bench where he could see the fountain and the flowers.

Only the birds and the splashing fountain disturbed the morning stillness. Demetrius thought about the events of the past weeks. He thought about Apollo, the great god of Antioch. He thought about the God his parents worshiped and especially about Paul and some of the things he had said about Jesus Christ. "How can Paul be so sure of what he believes?" Demetrius asked himself.

The stillness was broken by the sound of a footstep. Demetrius turned with a start and saw Paul walking toward him.

"I have been watching you, Demetrius," Paul said. "You look puzzled. Is something bothering you?"

Demetrius nodded, but he said nothing. He did not know if he dared to ask the questions that were on his mind.

"Don't be afraid of me," Paul reassured him.

"I—" Demetrius began, "I was wondering about Apollo and the God you believe in. Is your God really more powerful than Apollo? And if he is, why doesn't everybody believe in him?"

Paul didn't look surprised or angry. "Many people ask those questions, Demetrius. I can only tell you what I believe with my whole heart. The God of Jesus Christ is more powerful and wonderful than Apollo. No one can possibly imagine how great God is." Paul spoke quietly, but he said every word with certainty.

"Then why doesn't God make all people believe in him?"

"All people do not know about him, and it's not God's way to *make* people love him. He loves them, and as people come to know his love, they believe in him. More than that, they want to serve him."

Demetrius nodded slowly. He wished he could be absolutely sure that what Paul said was true.

Paul continued. "It isn't wrong to doubt, Demetrius. It's only wrong to pretend to believe something you really don't. God will speak to you, if you will listen. Keep trying to listen. And, Demetrius, I want you to be present at the gathering before I leave today. Will you?"

Demetrius looked at Paul in surprise. "But I thought only those who have been baptized were supposed to come. You mean it's all right for me to come too?"

"Yes," Paul answered, "I want you there. Now I must go back to the others."

Demetrius followed Paul into the house. His mother met him at the door. "There is bread and cheese for you," she said. "Then you may spend the time as you wish. Your father is not opening the shop until after Paul and the others have gone."

"Paul asked me to say good-bye when he left." Demetrius spoke proudly. "And I won't eat either. I will fast as you do before worship."

Helen frowned. "You're sure you want to?" she asked.

"Yes," Demetrius declared.

For a moment Helen did not speak. Then she smiled. "I won't urge you. When it's time for the service, I'll let you know. Then we'll go together to the edge of the city to say farewell."

It was nearly noon when all the followers gathered at the house where they often met for worship. Demetrius listened more carefully than ever before to the words read from the psalms and to Paul's farewell message. After the prayers, the members of the Antioch church followed Paul, Barnabas, and John Mark into the street. As they walked along they made quite a procession. Passers-by regarded them curiously.

When they neared the marketplace Demetrius saw some boys he knew.

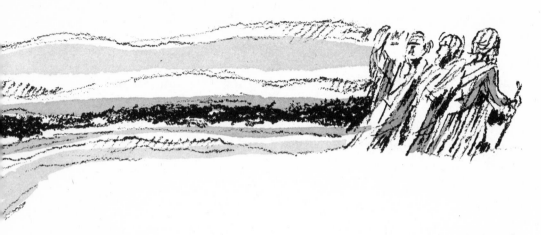

He started to hide himself in the crowd, but he changed his mind and waved to them instead.

"So you've joined up!" one of the boys shouted. "Watch out, Christian. Apollo doesn't like it when you ignore him!"

Demetrius kept right on walking, but Paul did not. He turned and faced the boys. "The time will come when Apollo will be forgotten," Paul began. Immediately some men who were passing by joined the group, curious to see what would happen next. Paul went on, "Believe in the true God who created you and loves you."

The men and boys jeered. "This is what you say, Christian! Now let's see you prove it."

Paul spoke again. "We need no proof, for we have met the living God in Jesus Christ, his Son. We are followers of this Jesus. Would that you were too!"

The men and boys shrugged their shoulders and laughed once more, but they did not answer.

At the edge of the city Paul, Barnabas, and John Mark said good-bye. "I will return when I can," Paul assured the followers in Antioch. "Farewell until we meet again." He looked around at the people until he saw Demetrius. "Farewell, Demetrius," Paul called. "May God grant you faith and peace."

Then the three men turned and started down the road. Demetrius watched until he could barely see them, walking steadily forward toward whatever adventure lay ahead. "I wonder if they will return," Demetrius said to himself. "I hope they will. God, they trust you. Please take care of them."

The group of followers began to separate, the men and boys going to their work, the women and girls back to their homes. "We will see you soon," they said to one another. "God be with Paul and Barnabas and John Mark. God be with us all."

Nicholas stayed with his family, staring down the road Paul had taken. "We'll miss them," he said.

"Yes," Helen answered. "But they are doing God's work, and I'm glad they're going."

Her husband nodded.

Back in the shop Nicholas and Demetrius worked steadily through the remainder of the day. Although they waited on customers and unpacked new shipments, neither one had his mind entirely on what he was doing. Toward the end of the afternoon, when the shop was empty and it was almost time to close for the night, Demetrius turned to his father. "This morning Paul said that God would speak to me, that he would help me to understand and believe. How will he speak?"

Nicholas stopped unpacking some vases that had just arrived. "I don't know, Demetrius," he replied. "God speaks in different ways. I think he speaks to many people through Paul and Barnabas. Perhaps he was speaking to you in this way."

Demetrius nodded. "Maybe—maybe that's why I think I want to be—" Demetrius paused, "I think I want to be a Christian."

Nicholas smiled. "I'm glad, son. Very glad." His smile changed to a broad grin. "And I'm glad you used that word! The people of Antioch may have given us a good name—Christian—those who belong to Jesus Christ."

Demetrius and his father closed the shop and started home just as the sunset was brightening the hills behind Antioch and painting golden streaks in the river. "Is Paul watching the sunset too?" Demetrius wondered. He hoped he was, for Paul seemed very near. "God, take care of Paul," he repeated. "Help him speak to others, and thank you for what he said to me."

The Bible Story of Paul

Although this story is not a true one, some events mentioned in it really happened. You can read about these in your Bible.

In *Acts 11:19–26* you will find an account of the work Paul and Barnabas did with the church in Antioch when it was first getting started. This passage also tells us that it was in Antioch that the followers of Jesus were first called Christian. Keep in mind as you read these verses that Saul and Paul are the same person.

Acts 12:25–13:3 gives an account of Barnabas, Paul, and John Mark coming to Antioch and being sent by the Antioch church to other countries to preach about Jesus Christ.

The words with which the leader began the service of worship in the story are from a Christian hymn which was perhaps used as early as Paul's day. The hymn is found in *Revelation 15:3*.

CARL OF WITTENBERG

CARL moved along the street as fast as he could, but it was not easy for an eleven-year-old to work his way through the crowd. People pushed him and bumped up against him. Fortunately, everyone was headed in the same direction on this cold December day in the town of Wittenberg, Germany. Instead of fighting the crowd Carl decided to let it carry him along.

When he reached the Elster Gate he looked around. "Everybody in Wittenberg must be here," he said to himself. But as he surveyed the crowd he realized that one group was missing—the priests of the church. Carl worked his way through the crowd until he could see the pile of logs and brush that was to become a huge bonfire. The fire had been ordered by the monk, Martin Luther. On it he intended to burn some of the most sacred documents of the church. And he was going to burn the order for his own excommunication.

Carl shivered, but not from the cold. What would happen after the books were burned and the logs became ashes? What would the church do to Martin Luther? What would the church do to Wittenberg? Would everyone be punished? Carl knew that the pope was angry, and the pope was very powerful.

The crowd grew still as everyone turned toward a procession of college and university students that was just coming into sight. At its head marched a man wearing the brown robe of a monk and carrying an armload of books and documents. Carl knew this was Martin Luther.

The procession moved steadily toward the center of the crowd. The monk nodded toward one of the students who stepped forward and kindled a flame. As the fire brightened, Dr. Luther walked up and threw the books and papers into it. Still there was silence except for the crackling of the fire. Carl watched breathlessly. The monk bowed his head and said something Carl could not hear. "He's praying," Carl realized.

When Dr. Luther raised his head the students began to cheer. Others, including Carl, joined the shouting and fell in line behind the students as they marched around the fire. The monk gave the fire one last glance and left.

Slowly the crowd broke up. There was nothing more to see. Martin Luther had done what he said he would. He had burned the canon law of the church and the excommunication order issued by the pope. He had declared his independence from the authority of the church in a way that the pope would never forgive or forget.

Carl watched the people as they went back to their work or their homes. When the crowd had thinned he started toward his school, his mind full of what he had just seen.

Most of the other boys were already in the schoolroom when Carl arrived. They were too busy talking with one another to notice him or to notice Herr Schumann, the teacher, as he entered the room a few moments later. But Herr Schumann's voice brought all the boys to their feet.

"You are here," he said, motioning for them to sit down. "This is good. But I can see your minds are not on your lessons!"

The boys looked uncomfortable. Carl tried to remember what the lessons were about, but he could not. Fortunately, the teacher's first question was about something else.

"Do you know what you saw this morning?" he asked.

For a moment no one spoke. Then Carl answered, "Yes, sir, Dr. Luther burned the books he did not like. He burned the order of excommunication too."

The teacher nodded. "That's right. Into that fire Martin Luther threw the law of the church and the order for his own excommunication. The pope will not overlook what Dr. Luther has done. The fire has burned down, but the meaning of that fire has not."

"Is there going to be trouble?" one of the boys asked.

"There is," Herr Schumann replied. "I'm sure there will be trouble for Martin Luther and perhaps for all of us in Wittenberg."

The boys looked at one another uneasily. They remembered what the pope could do. He was a person who could speak for God himself. Why, he might even close their church and fine their parents.

"Sir," Carl spoke anxiously, "what will happen next? What will the pope do?"

"That I cannot say," Herr Schumann answered. "We can only wait and see. But this I know: Martin Luther will act too. He knows what he is doing and why he is doing it." The teacher stopped suddenly as though he had said more than he intended.

Carl thought again of the man in the brown robe who had marched at the head of the students. He had indeed looked as if he knew what he was doing and why. Carl wanted to see more of him; he wanted to know more about him. What would this bold monk do next? And what would the pope do?

Carl's thoughts were interrupted by the teacher. "Now it's time we put our minds on our lessons. It will be soon enough to worry about the future when we know what that future is."

Herr Schumann Explains

As the days passed, Carl became aware of an uneasy feeling in Wittenberg. Small groups gathered in the streets to talk about Martin Luther and his stand against the powerful church. Rumors spread around the town that Luther had been summoned to appear before a meeting of all the princes of Germany. Another rumor followed that the summons had been dropped. No one was sure what was happening.

Stories were told of other men who had spoken out against the church, especially of John Huss who was burned to death for his beliefs. Luther was called a follower of Huss, and some said that the monk would surely die in the same way. Carl shuddered at the thought of this.

He wished he could find out more about this man who was so different from the other monks and teachers in the university. What made him do the things he did? If these things were wrong, why did the students listen to him and follow him?

Carl did not know where to go for answers to his questions. His mother and father refused to mention Luther's name. Since the day of the bonfire, his school teacher had said nothing that would encourage Carl to ask about the monk.

Then one day about four months after the fire, the whole town of Wittenberg learned that Dr. Luther had been summoned by the emperor to a meeting of the ruling princes of Germany. There he would be made to answer for his books and teachings.

Many people urged him not to go. They said he would never reach the meeting alive, that the meeting was only a trick to get him away from his friends so he could be killed.

On the morning Luther left, Carl and some of his classmates stood with the crowd that watched the monk and three companions climb into the two-wheeled, wooden cart in which they would make the journey. Just as they were about to set off, a man dressed in the brightly colored uniform of an emperor's herald rode up, carrying a yellow silk banner that was embroidered with a two-headed black eagle and the royal coat of arms.

Holding the banner high before him, the herald urged his horse into position at the head of the party. Luther waved to the crowd, and the horses trotted off. Carl watched as long as he could see the cart and its passengers. He felt uneasy. Perhaps Dr. Luther would never return to Wittenberg.

"Would you like to go along?" a familiar voice asked.

Carl looked up in surprise. There beside him stood his teacher. The boy did not know how to answer. He would like to go, but he would be afraid. Nothing like this had ever happened in Wittenberg.

"*I* would like to go," Herr Schumann said, almost to himself. "Dr. Luther is teaching us a great many things that we should have known all along."

Carl was startled by the words. His teacher must agree with Martin Luther! Feeling easier now about stating the questions that were troubling him, Carl asked, "Will Martin Luther be killed?"

"I don't know," Herr Schumann answered. "He may be. Now the emperor is against him, as well as the church. He is considered a dangerous man because he is encouraging people to ask questions and to think for themselves. The emperor may not dare to let him live."

"Sir," Carl said hesitantly, "what does Dr. Luther teach? What does he say that the church doesn't like?"

The teacher looked at his pupil. "Why do you want to know?"

"Because Dr. Luther seems so different from the other monks. I wish I could know him. I wanted to hear him in the church, but my father said his teachings weren't for the ears of good people, and we should be loyal to the church and the pope."

"Your father may be right, but if you want to know why Luther is in trouble, I'll try to tell you. Let's go over to the schoolroom, and I'll explain some of his teachings."

This was the first time Carl had ever been in the schoolroom without the other boys. The seats looked very empty, and his teacher looked very serious.

"You remember," Herr Schumann began, "when Dr. Luther said the pope had no right to sell indulgences to people? You remember when he nailed on the cathedral door his arguments against buying forgiveness for sins?"

Carl nodded. He remembered how this had surprised and infuriated some of the people of Wittenberg, and how it had pleased others. But Carl had not thought much about it. Teachers often put notices on the church door. It was their way of bringing certain important matters to one another's attention.

Herr Schumann continued. "That was the beginning, for you see, Carl, the attack on indulgences was more than a protest against this practice. Dr. Luther was saying that the church does not have the right to do whatever it wishes. The church is not all-powerful."

"But what is more powerful than the church?" Carl asked in surprise.

"Dr. Luther says that God is—God as he speaks through the Bible. The church must not do anything that is contrary to the teachings of the Bible. And the Bible teaches that only God's love, as we know it through Jesus Christ, can forgive us when we do wrong."

Carl was puzzled. "The church tells us what's in the Bible, doesn't it?"

His teacher shook his head. "Yes and no. The church has been telling us only what it wants us to know of the Bible. It has not given us a chance to read and find out for ourselves."

"But why?" Carl asked.

"I can only tell you what I think—I think the church is afraid. It's afraid of new ideas that the people might get if they read the Bible for themselves. Perhaps it's afraid it will lose its power over us."

"Can I read the Bible?" Carl asked, suddenly eager to know more about this important book.

"No, Carl, at least not now," Herr Schumann answered. "But the time may come when everyone will be able to read it. This is what Dr. Luther believes must happen, and I believe it too."

Herr Schumann stood up. "Martin Luther is in trouble because he has opposed the teaching of the church, and the church wants to silence him. I hope he returns to us safely, but I am afraid for him—very much afraid."

Carl stood too. He knew his teacher was ready to leave. "Thank you, sir," he said gratefully. "I hope Dr. Luther comes back soon."

A month passed. The trees in Wittenberg were green and spring flowers were blooming. One day just as Carl and his friends were leaving school, a horseman raced through the town crying, "Martin Luther has been kidnapped!" When the man was questioned he explained that on the way home Luther was attacked in the woods and taken away. Now no one knew where he was.

Carl looked at his teacher who stood in the doorway, his face pale and angry. "Have they killed him?" the boy asked anxiously.

"I don't know, but I'll try to find out what happened," Herr Schumann replied. "I'll tell you boys tomorrow. Now run along."

That night Carl slept fitfully and slipped out of bed as soon as daylight came. He dressed quickly, left the house, and hurried toward the school. To his surprise, he met Herr Schumann in the street.

His teacher was just as surprised to see him. "Good morning, Carl. You're up early!" he exclaimed.

"I couldn't sleep," Carl answered. "Did you find out anything?"

"Not very much," Herr Schumann shook his head. "That is, not very much about the kidnapping. But I did learn about Dr. Luther's appearance before the emperor and the church leaders. He stood up alone before them and refused to take back anything he had said or written. His friends who were there say he was magnificent."

"But was he really kidnapped?" Carl persisted.

The teacher nodded. "On the way home, while he was riding through a dense section of woods, some men fell upon the cart, threw Luther to the ground, and then made off with him. The friends who were riding with him were overpowered. All of them have returned with the same story."

"But why doesn't someone do something?" Carl burst out.

"What can we do? We can't search all Germany," Herr Schumann explained. "No one knows where to look. And," he added sadly, "by now Martin Luther may be dead."

The teacher started to turn away and then stopped. "Carl, we won't hold classes today. I want to talk to some people. Tell the other boys what I've told you and that I will see them tomorrow."

"I will," Carl promised. Slowly he walked down the street wondering if he would ever see Dr. Luther again.

Carl continued to wonder for many days and weeks, for there was no further word about what had happened to the Wittenberg monk.

But although Luther had disappeared, his teaching and preaching were not forgotten. The kidnapping had made some of his followers angry and determined to continue the protest that Luther had started. Other people who were loyal to the church declared that Luther had received the punishment he deserved.

Soon trouble developed between the two groups. One morning some students and townspeople, who declared they were doing what Luther would want, entered a small church and tore down all the images of the saints.

A few days later another group entered a church building and destroyed the altar. Riots started, and priests became afraid to appear in the streets without a bodyguard. Mothers kept their children indoors. Loyal church families hesitated to attend mass. No one knew when the troublemakers would strike next or what they would do.

One day the following winter, as Carl and the other boys were leaving school, they heard a commotion in the street. The cause, they discovered, was a group of men and students marching along, with one student carrying an image of a saint and another a Bible. They pointed first to the saint and shouted, "Not this." Then they pointed to the Bible and shouted, "But this."

Herr Schumann looked at the noisy crowd and shook his head. "If only Luther would return," he said. "We need him badly."

Carl heard the words and was too surprised to remember to address his teacher properly. "What did you say?" he asked in amazement. "Is Martin Luther alive?"

The teacher answered quickly, "Hush, Carl. Come inside."

Out of earshot of the other boys, Herr Schumann spoke again. "I should not have said what I did. Yes, Dr. Luther is alive. He has been writing to us, and there is no doubt that the letters come from him. We think now that he was kidnapped by friends for his own protection."

Carl found this hard to believe. "Why hasn't everyone been told?" he asked. "Why is it a secret?"

"Luther's safety is at stake," the teacher answered. "His enemies have guessed the truth, but they aren't sure. Now the secret is yours, too, and you must keep it."

"I will," Carl promised. "I will. Maybe when Dr. Luther learns what's happening, he'll come back."

Luther Speaks Again

The situation in Wittenberg did not improve. The town council could not stop the destruction, the riots, or the attack on the churches, and the people became more afraid. Friends of Luther, who knew how these events would disturb him, decided that only one course of action was possible. They would have to ask him to return.

Some men who knew his secret hiding place took the message to him. Luther wanted to be with his people, and when he heard how serious the trouble in Wittenberg was, he knew he must return, regardless of the dangers to himself. With the help of friends, he slipped quietly back into the town.

One spring morning, about a year after the news of the kidnapping had first come to the startled people of Wittenberg, Martin Luther, straight and stern-faced, stepped into the pulpit of one of the churches. In the rear of the church Carl waited eagerly to hear what he would say. Would he condemn the emperor and the pope? Would he scold the people for the way they had been behaving?

Luther did not scold, but he spoke sternly about the need for patience, about the danger of trying to force people into believing what they do not understand. "You cannot change the minds of people by driving them from their churches or breaking their altars," Luther declared. "This is not the spirit in which the Christian treats his neighbor."

"He talks as if he cares about every single person here," Carl said to himself. "No wonder people listen and believe him."

When the service was over Carl walked slowly out into the street. He had made a decision he intended to keep. He was going to join Luther's followers and learn all he could from them about God and God's love for his people. Carl knew he had one friend to whom he could turn for help—his own teacher.

The boy stood and watched the people as they came from the church. Some looked very happy. A few kept their eyes lowered and hurried away as though they were ashamed to be seen. When his teacher appeared, Carl walked over to him.

"Yes, Carl," Herr Schumann greeted him. "Do you want to see me?"

"I just wanted you to know—I'm glad Dr. Luther is back. And I'd like to know more about his teaching. How can I start learning? Will you help me?"

"I'll certainly try, Carl," the teacher answered. "Dr. Luther has written some things you can study. But most important of all is a book that you soon will be able to read for yourself. While he was in hiding Martin Luther translated the New Testament into our own language. Now everyone will be able to read the story of Jesus Christ for himself."

"Is the Bible hard to read?" Carl asked cautiously.

"It isn't easy, and you may have to work hard. But anyone who wants to badly enough can read it, think about it, and hear Jesus Christ speak to him through its pages."

"I do want to, and I'll try," Carl promised.

Herr Schumann was silent for a moment. Then he pointed in the direction of the Elster Gate. "Remember the bonfire, Carl?"

Carl nodded, wondering why his teacher had suddenly changed the subject.

"A fire was started there not very long ago. That fire was not just burning papers; it was burning the authority of the church—authority that was being used to keep the people from seeking the truth. For a time some of us were afraid that fire would die out. Fortunately we were wrong. That fire will keep on burning wherever men like Martin Luther —and perhaps you, too, Carl—try to know God's truth. It's a fire we must keep alight."

Herr Schumann nodded in the direction of the church door. "There he goes—Martin Luther, the lighter of fires. May God give him courage and patience and faith. He will need them all in the work he has ahead."

Carl watched as Martin Luther, surrounded by a group of friends, walked away from the church building. "He is strong," Carl thought, "and brave. I'm glad I know him. Maybe someday I can work with him. I'd like to; I'd like to very much!"

JOHN ELIOT
Apostle to the Indians

JOHN Eliot stood in front of the church on the common of Newtown, Massachusetts, talking with his friend Thomas Hooker. Around them was a large group of men, women, and children. Nearby, sheep, cows, and pigs were moving about restlessly, their cries rising above the voices of the people.

"Thomas, my friend," Eliot said, "I shall miss you. I wish you didn't feel you had to go."

"I wish we weren't leaving," Hooker replied, "but I know it's the right thing to do. If we remain here near Boston, we will have less and less say about our own affairs as a church. So we will find a new home for ourselves in a place where we have the freedom I know God intended men to have."

John Eliot sighed. "You are right to go, even though I know it's hard. May God protect you on your journey."

The two men shook hands. "May God protect you too," Hooker replied. Then he mounted his horse, waved to the waiting people, and rode away from the church. The group fell into line behind him. Slowly the procession moved forward.

John Eliot watched until the people and animals had disappeared into the forest. Then he mounted his own horse and turned in the direction of Roxbury. His thoughts were troubled. Should he, too, be leaving? He agreed with Thomas Hooker and his parishioners that all important decisions should be made by the people in their own congregations. Since

more power was being taken by those in authority, perhaps the only thing to do was leave and find new places to live in the American wilderness.

"But I'm sure I'm right in remaining," John Eliot said to himself finally. "Roxbury is my home. The people have chosen me as their minister. I have work to do in my own church and with the Indians among us who do not know God."

As John Eliot jogged along the trail that wound through the forest and across the corners of cleared farmland, he thought about the Massachusetts Indians. He felt he must serve them, even though he did not yet know how. He remembered one of the first scenes that had greeted him after his arrival from England. A group of Indians had been bartering with the English settlers, offering beautiful beadwork, wild turkeys, and animal skins for the white man's iron plows, cloth, and muskets. Neither

Englishmen nor Indians could speak the others' language, but the trade was successfully made. "You can buy and sell in sign language," Eliot said to himself. "But how can you speak of God's great love unless you have words?" Eliot knew he must learn the Algonquin language if he were to tell the Indians about God, but where could he find someone to teach him?

This question continued to puzzle John Eliot as he went on with his work in Roxbury, preaching and working among the people of his parish. Then one day when he was reading in his study there was a knock at the door. "Come in," he said. The door opened and a tall Indian entered. He was clearly an Indian of importance, dressed in fringed deerskin, moccasins, and a beautifully beaded headband. With him were two Indian boys wearing English clothes.

"I am Waban," the Indian introduced himself in English, "chief of my tribe. And these are my nephews. They want to go to the white man's school and learn about the white man's God. I have heard that you are our friend, and so I have come to you for help."

"You are a Christian?" John Eliot asked in surprise.

"No, but I, too, wish to learn more about your religion. I like what I have heard."

John Eliot nodded. This was welcome news indeed. He looked at the two boys.

"I wish we could care for them here in my home," he said to Waban. "But my family is large. I know we can find a good place for them, however. They can stay here for tonight and start school tomorrow. Then I'll see that they go to a family where they will be well treated."

"Thank you," Waban answered. "You stay and work hard," he told the boys. "Now I must leave. I live many miles from here."

"Just a minute," Eliot said as a thought struck him. "Chief Waban, I want to speak your language so that I can tell your people about the white man's God. You know some English. Will you teach me?"

Waban shook his head. "I live too far from you, and my people need me. But you have helped me, and I will help you. I know of a teacher. His name is Cockinoë. He learned to speak English from those who took him captive in a war. Now he is at Mr. Calcutt's home in Dorchester. You ask Mr. Calcutt for Cockinoë."

Cockinoë

John Eliot lost no time acting on Waban's suggestion. Early the next morning he left on horseback for Dorchester. He had no trouble finding Mr. Calcutt's home, a big house on the edge of town.

When he knocked on the door, he was greeted by a young Indian dressed in English clothing.

"You are Cockinoë?" Mr. Eliot asked.

The young man nodded. "I am Cockinoë," he replied in English.

"Chief Waban told me I would find you here. He said you spoke English and could teach me to speak your language. I have come to ask you to do this if Mr. Calcutt is willing."

Cockinoë looked surprised and troubled. "I do not want to leave Mr. Calcutt," he answered. "He is good to me, and I am happy here. But I will do what Mr. Calcutt says."

John Eliot entered the house and found himself in a large room that was furnished with chests and tables from England. On the floor was a rug, an unusual luxury in a Massachusetts home.

Cockinoë disappeared through a door, but returned almost immediately with a tall, well-dressed man who smiled when he saw John Eliot.

"You are known to me by your reputation," Mr. Calcutt said. "What brings you to Dorchester?"

John Eliot explained what he wanted.

As he listened, Mr. Calcutt seemed more and more surprised. "You've chosen a difficult task for yourself," he said. "The Algonquin speech is very unlike English and very hard for Englishmen to learn. But I've heard of your good work in Roxbury and of your interest in the Indian people. If you need Cockinoë, he may go with you, much as I hate to lose him." Mr. Calcutt looked toward Cockinoë and added, "He may go if he is willing."

For a moment Cockinoë was silent; then he shook his head. "Mr. Calcutt has given me a home. He treats me as a friend even though I'm a slave. I wish to stay with him."

John Eliot nodded. He could understand why an Indian would want to stay with a man whom he liked and trusted. "Cockinoë," Eliot said, "I don't want you to come against your wishes, but I need you. I promise you a good home, with a chance to learn and the freedom to return to Mr. Calcutt if you don't enjoy your life in Roxbury. Will you give this a try?"

Cockinoë looked from Mr. Calcutt to John Eliot. It was a hard decision to make. "I will go," he said. "You want to help my people. I will teach you to speak our words."

A Sick Boy

For several years John Eliot and Cockinoë worked together. Often they started early in the morning and continued until late at night.

There were times when Mr. Eliot wondered if his tongue would ever get around the strange new sounds it had to pronounce and if his mind would ever remember the words it had to learn. Many words were long because the Indians did not make new ones for new meanings. They simply put a lot of old words together. "Our love" in Algonquin was "noowomantainmoonkamnonash." Sometimes there was no word into which an English word could be translated. But gradually John Eliot did learn to speak and to think in Algonquin.

While he was studying he continued to be minister of the church in Roxbury. There were sermons to prepare, calls to make, weddings to perform, and all too many funerals in his community. More than one smallpox epidemic broke out and took lives of children and adults alike. Whenever help of any kind was needed, the people turned to John Eliot.

But his parish soon spread far beyond Roxbury. Before he had learned to speak the Algonquin language easily, the Indians who heard of his interest in them began coming to him whenever they were in trouble.

On one occasion a chief begged him to see his son who was very ill with smallpox. John Eliot found the boy flushed with fever, lying on a mat in the chief's wigwam. Beside him was a medicine man, a powwow, who shrieked and shouted, trying to frighten away the evil spirits that were thought to cause the disease.

Immediately Eliot ordered the powwow to leave. "The boy cannot rest while you're here," he said.

The powwow angrily told Eliot that he would not leave and that he would call down the evil spirits upon his head.

But Eliot insisted. "If you do not go immediately, the boy will surely die."

The boy's father looked worried. He was afraid to offend the powwow, yet he trusted Mr. Eliot. He made up his mind. "Go," he told the medicine man.

The powwow raised his fists and shouted louder than ever, but as he did so, he backed through the opening in the wigwam.

John Eliot sat beside the sick boy. Now the wigwam was quiet, and before long the boy slept.

As Eliot left he turned to the anxious chief and said, "I hope your son will be well soon. There are no evil spirits that have to be frightened away. Believe instead in God who loves your boy even more than you or I do."

The chief nodded. Eliot mounted his horse and rode toward home. He knew he might be in serious trouble. The power of the powwows over the Indians was great. If the boy died, the medicine men could turn the people against Eliot and perhaps put a stop to the work he had scarcely begun.

After many days the chief's son recovered, to Eliot's great joy. Not only was the boy well, but perhaps the hold of the powwows on the people would begin to break.

First Sermons

At last the time came when John Eliot felt he was ready to preach his first sermon to the Indians. He worked hard on it, rehearsing every word he would say. Then he asked a chief who lived near Dorchester to let him preach to some of his people. The chief agreed and gathered a small group to hear "the good Mr. Eliot."

As Eliot faced the silent Indians who sat before him, he asked for God's help. Then he began his sermon, speaking every word slowly and carefully. When he had finished, the Indians stood up and left. John Eliot knew he had failed to reach them. Had he been so worried about speaking correctly that he had failed to say what he really meant? He was discouraged and disappointed, but he knew what he had to do.

For several weeks more he practiced, preaching to Cockinoë who listened critically, helped him to smooth out the rough places, and corrected his pronunciation. Some friends who heard of the Indians' response to the first sermon told John Eliot he was wasting his energy. The Indians did not deserve all this hard work. But John Eliot knew

they did. He firmly believed that the church was not just for the white man. It was for the Indian too.

At last, Mr. Eliot was ready to try once more. This time he went to Chief Waban's village.

"The people are waiting," Waban told him when he arrived. "I have said you are a fine man and our friend. Now you speak to them about your God."

As John Eliot rose to preach, the memory of his first sermon went through his mind. Would he fail again? "No," he told himself. The Indians were ready. With God's help he would be ready too.

For an hour and a quarter he preached. He spoke of the ten commandments and how important it was to obey them. He told of Jesus Christ who came so that all men might know God. Then he stopped, hardly prepared for what happened.

The Indians did not remain silent. Nor did they leave. Instead they began to ask questions, one after another. Each question showed a great eagerness to know more. Are the commandments for Indians too? Do good children have to obey fathers if fathers are wicked? How can God be everywhere? Does God really love us?

Eliot tried to answer the questions clearly and simply. The people gave him all their attention. When at last he stopped, he knew that this time his sermon had meant something to his hearers. He could now preach to them in their own language. His work as a missionary to them could really begin.

A Bible for the Indians

The work did begin. Tribes near Roxbury asked John Eliot to speak to them. Invitations arrived from more distant places. The Roxbury minister rode miles on horseback in all kinds of weather. Often he had to cross dangerous streams. More than once he was soaked through by rain and covered by snow. But nothing stopped him, and gradually he became known far and near as the "apostle to the Indians."

Soon, however, Eliot realized that preaching was not enough. He could be with the different Indian groups only once in a while and only for short periods of time. He must help them to teach themselves. The Bible in their own language was the answer.

"It's a big book!" Cockinoë said when Eliot told him his idea. But the task of translation needed to be done, and John Eliot undertook it.

He undertook another project as well, that of starting communities of "praying Indians," as the groups of Indian Christians came to be called. Those who had become followers of Jesus Christ would be invited to these communities, and they would live together, have their own church, and govern themselves. When Chief Waban heard of the idea he and his people were eager for a "praying town." So were many other Indians who were being persecuted by the powwows because they had become Christians.

John Eliot looked for a place where a "praying town" could be started. He found a lovely section of country with rolling meadows that were right for corn and the few other crops the Indians raised. Chief Waban was delighted with the location and asked that the place be given the Indian name "Natick," which meant "place of hills."

Work was begun to make the town ready for its new inhabitants. John Eliot helped to lay out streets, construct the central meeting house, and mark the plots of land each Indian would have for his own.

When all was ready a meeting was held. The Indians were given ownership of their land "forever," and many of the white men welcomed them into the fellowship of Christian people. A few years later, an Indian minister was ordained in the Natick church. The Indian Christians were happy, and John Eliot felt that something had been started that could be continued all across the country. Soon there were a number of praying towns located around Boston, and their future seemed very bright.

During all this time John Eliot had been working on his translation of the New Testament. In 1661 he completed his task and presented some of the first copies to his friend Chief Waban of Natick. "The word of life is now your own," Eliot told him.

Two years later the Old Testament was printed and bound with the New. On the title page were the words:

UP-BIBLUM GOD
NUKKONE TESTAMENT
WUSKU TESTAMENT

This was the first translation of the Bible into any American Indian language and the first Bible to be printed anywhere on the North American continent.

John Eliot also translated a psalm book and a primer. He managed all this while he preached in his own church, rode mile after mile to speak to Indians who were not in praying towns, conducted weddings and funerals, helped to start a seminary at Harvard University to train Indian ministers, and acted as spokesman for the Indians when trouble arose with the colonists.

"I Despise the English"

Eliot's concern for the Indians was shared by a number of the English colonists, but not enough to prevent incident after incident in which Indians were mistreated. As a result, hatred of the white men grew through the years and flared up in many places. Agreements with the Indians were broken, and Indians responded by burning the settlers' homes. Indians scalped white men, and very often white men scalped Indians. Tension grew slowly and steadily.

Into this situation came King Philip, a powerful Indian chief. He believed the new world belonged to his people, and he did not want it settled by outsiders who took land and built forts and homes. King Philip had the support of a number of Indian tribes that shared his hatred of the white men and his determination to drive them away.

For a long time there was a feeling of fear in the air, of something

about to happen, something tragic and dangerous. But no one was sure when trouble would come or how it would start.

Then one day the news was heard in Boston that King Philip had killed an Indian as a white men's spy. Immediately the white men responded by killing some of Philip's subjects, which incited Philip, in turn, to capture a town and murder seven white people. This was a declaration of war!

The officials in Boston wondered what to do. They were frightened and worried. They knew there was no way to guard all the settlers against Indian attacks. Many people lived outside the towns in log houses, which were easily set on fire by flaming arrows. Men had to leave their wives and children unprotected if they were to work their farms and care for their livestock. While the men were gone, the women and children could easily be killed or taken captive.

The Boston officials decided to ask John Eliot, now seventy-one years old, to make the difficult and dangerous trip through Indian country

to King Philip's headquarters to try to persuade him to stop the fighting. John Eliot agreed to go.

It was a strange, frightening journey, unlike any trip he had ever made. He and his two companions passed farm houses and stables burned to the ground. There were no signs of the people who had lived there or of the animals that should have been in the fields. The men sensed that they were being watched every step along the way, but they could see no one. Several times Eliot's companions wanted to turn back, but Eliot would not listen to them.

"We must go on," he said. "We must try, even at the risk of our own lives. If we fail, many people will die."

Finally, they came to a good-sized Indian village with many wigwams. "Here surely we will learn news of Philip," Eliot told his companions. But the wigwams were empty. There was a terrifying silence in the forest. Then, just as the three men were about to go on, they were surrounded by a group of armed warriors.

"John Eliot," one of the Indians said, "our orders are to take you alone to King Philip."

"I will not go without the men who are with me," Eliot replied.

"They will be safe," the Indians said. "You will find them here when you return."

Eliot looked at the warriors and believed them. Silently, he nodded to his companions and rode away with the Indians.

It was not much farther to King Philip's headquarters. As Eliot approached he saw a large, well-constructed building. He was taken to the doorway and ordered to wait. There he remained for a long time—"Long enough to make me worry if I had wanted to," Eliot said afterward. Then he was ushered inside.

King Philip stood before him, tall and haughty in his battle dress. Over his shoulders he wore a cape of brightly colored feathers. On his head was a high headdress. A war knife, unsheathed, hung on his chest.

"Speak," King Philip commanded. "You must wish to see me to have traveled so far." There was no other greeting, no welcome.

John Eliot looked at Philip, and then, aware of the stern, cold look in the Indian's eyes, he began to talk. He told of the Englishmen's desire for peace and of their willingness to make a treaty that would respect the lands and rights of both Indians and white men.

The expression on King Philip's face did not change, but he watched every movement of Eliot's lips.

When Eliot stopped, King Philip remained silent for a moment, not because he was unsure of what he was going to say, but to dramatize his power and the firmness of his words.

"I will make no treaty with your government," he said finally. "Any treaty would be broken. I will speak only with your King of England himself."

"But there isn't time," Eliot pleaded. "It will take months to receive word from England."

"Then you know my answer," King Philip responded.

Eliot tried once more. "If you will not listen to me, listen to another King who is greater than the King of England. He is the great God of love who says that all men are brothers and all men should live in peace. Hear him, and let us have peace."

"What kind of King do you talk about who lets his subjects kill my people and steal our lands!"

John Eliot became very earnest. "If you will not listen to me, take me as your hostage. I will stay here as a guarantee that what I say is true."

"No," King Philip said. "Now go. Tell your government I despise it. I am through with you."

There was nothing to do but return to Boston. John Eliot found his companions where he had left them, and together they retraced their steps through the deserted countryside. King Philip's War was on.

Kill the Indians!

The war was a cruel one, with Indians and settlers alike killing and plundering. Colonists' homes were burned to the ground. Indian women and children were shot in front of their wigwams. It was a time of terror, and no one could be sure he was safe.

The Indians in the praying towns suffered more than others. Many of the English settlers, full of hatred for any Indian, accused them of spying for King Philip. This led to an order that the Indians must stay inside their homes and not leave for any purpose. When John Eliot pointed out that this meant starvation because they had no food stored away, some of the colonists replied, "Better to starve them than to let them kill us."

King Philip was also suspicious of the praying Indians. Because he knew they were loyal to the colonists, he showed them no mercy. As the war continued, conditions grew worse. Finally, the Christian Indians were driven from their homes and held as prisoners by the English soldiers. They had little food, and many were sick.

John Eliot did all he could to help them, often buying food with his own money. He talked with them and tried to give them encouragement. He talked with the English settlers, but nothing he could say convinced them that these Indians were loyal.

One evening when Eliot was working in his study, he heard a soft tapping at the window. He looked up with a start. When he saw nothing he returned to his work. A few moments later the tapping was repeated. This time he went to the window and saw the face of an Indian pressed against the glass. It was a young man from Natick.

John Eliot let the man in. "Chief Waban sent me," the Indian said quickly. "All the people have been taken away by the soldiers."

"No!" Eliot exclaimed. "Not the Natick Indians! They are loyal to the last child."

"You know this," the Indian answered, "but the soldiers do not."

"Where have they been taken?" Eliot asked.

"I will show you," the Indian replied.

Hurriedly Eliot collected some food, clothing, and medicine, and loaded them on a horse.

The Indian led John Eliot to a place on the Charles River where about two hundred people from Natick were huddled together, trying to protect themselves from the cold. The soldiers had given them no time to pack any of their possessions. Some had grabbed a little food as they were rushed away. A few had managed to bring copies of their Bibles. Nearby were the soldiers, laughing and talking around a small campfire.

John Eliot set to work distributing the few supplies he had among those who needed them most. He talked with his people, trying to comfort them, and promising to bring more food and medicine as soon as he possibly could.

Suddenly Eliot stopped to listen. The noise he was hearing was the creaking of boats pulling up against the bank of the river. Scarcely able to believe what was happening, he stood by helplessly as the Indians were herded onto boats that were to take them to small, desolate Deer Island out in the bay.

Chief Waban was the last to board. Now it was he who gave courage to Eliot. "Don't fear for us," he said. "We will be loyal to the truth you have taught us. We know God cares for us, and we will not be afraid."

John Eliot remained on the shore, listening in the darkness as the boats moved slowly out into the river. Then, sadly, he turned and rode back to Roxbury.

During the weeks that followed, Eliot redoubled his efforts to help not only the Natick Indians on Deer Island, but all who were captured and left homeless when their villages were destroyed.

The war went on, but gradually the settlers began to forge ahead. In one battle King Philip's headquarters were taken, although he escaped. Over a thousand Indians were killed, and six hundred were captured. Against the vigorous protest of John Eliot, the captured Indians were sold as slaves.

"Slavery is wrong," Eliot declared. "Every person, no matter who he is, is important to God. You cannot, you must not do this."

But his protests were in vain. By now the hatred of the Indians was so strong that the colonists were determined to destroy them or reduce them to slavery.

The Natick Indians on Deer Island became objects of the fierce hatred of some of the white men, and one night a mob gathered to attack the island and kill every Indian on it.

Hearing what was to happen, Eliot desperately gathered a group of men he could count on and rushed down to the wharf where the mob had assembled. He stood before the angry settlers and pleaded with them. "You are violating God's law as well as man's if you do this thing. Go home. Do not start something you will always regret."

The mob laughed and jeered until Eliot could not be heard. "Look at him!" the men shouted. "John Eliot, lover of the Indians. Maybe he forgets what they have done to us. Let's string him up! That will keep him quiet!"

The angry men surged toward Eliot, then stopped suddenly as a new

sound was heard above the shouts and the slapping of the water against the wharf. It was the sound of marching feet—soldiers who were no lovers of the Indians, but who were intent on keeping order.

The leaders of the mob realized that they were outnumbered. There was a quick scrambling, and those who had come to kill the Indians disappeared as fast as they could.

Tragedy had been averted, not only for John Eliot, but for the Deer Island captives whom he loved more than he did his own life. But for how long? Eliot wondered as he rode wearily back home.

Throughout the winter the Roxbury preacher saw that food, clothing, and medicine were taken to Deer Island regularly. Then as King Philip was driven closer to defeat, and as more Indians proved themselves loyal as scouts and spies, the settlers began to be less hostile toward them. John Eliot secured permission to move those on Deer Island to the land of a friendly farmer where they could grow some crops and help to support themselves.

Finally, the war came to an end. Gradually villages were resettled, and those who had lived in Natick were able to return and start life again. John Eliot rejoiced, but there was sorrow mixed with his happiness, for many of his friends had not lived through the attack and the hard winter on the Island. Chief Waban had survived, and although he was now an old man, he was able to help his people as they rebuilt their homes and replanted their farms.

All Men Belong to God

John Eliot was an old man himself by this time, but he was not ready to retire. He began working on a revision of his Indian translation of the Bible. In 1680 the revised New Testament was completed and published. "I want to see this finished before I die," he told a friend. "I will depart gladly if I can leave behind the word of God."

Five years later he achieved his wish. The revision of the Old Testament was finished.

More years passed. Now John Eliot could not make the long trips on horseback to visit his Indian friends. He had an assistant minister in his church in Roxbury to help him with his preaching and church work. But he still continued to write and help as much as his strength would permit.

One day in May of 1690 a friend came to call on him. John Eliot greeted him warmly, visited with him for a few minutes, and then asked the friend to leave him alone for a time. Perhaps Eliot knew that his strength was running out. That same afternoon, while he was teaching a blind Indian boy to read, he died.

For fifty-seven years the people of Roxbury had known and loved John Eliot as their minister. For almost as long the Indians of eastern Massachusetts had known and loved him too. From John Eliot, Indians and white men alike learned that all men belong to God. They learned that the church is too big to be limited to any one race or group of people. In its fellowship belong all who love and serve God.

FRONTIER PREACHER

THE boys grouped around Joseph Rieger looked worried. "Did we get it right that time?" one of them asked anxiously.

"Exactly," Joseph replied. "A little more work, and you will pass the catechism examination without any trouble."

"I hope so," one of the other boys declared. "But I wish I could remember it as well as you do. It doesn't seem fair. You're a Catholic, and you know our Lutheran catechism better than we do!"

"Maybe I try harder," Joseph grinned. Then his smile faded. "Maybe I believe it more," he added to himself. "And if I do, whatever will become of me?"

When his Protestant friends had left, carrying their catechism books with them, Joseph sat thinking for a long time. The more he thought, the bigger his problem looked. No one knew that he no longer believed what his own church taught, that he wanted to be a Protestant. And there was no one with whom he dared talk. He felt troubled and alone.

His parents had died when he was very young, and he had been sent from their home in Germany to live with an aunt and uncle in France who now cared for him and sent him to school. They were proud of his alert mind. He was bright enough to be a priest, they said. His quickness as a student was responsible for the situation in which he now found himself. It had led the Protestant boys at the school he attended to ask him to help them with their catechism. As a result, he had come to believe the teachings of the Protestant church. What could he do?

He decided that for the time being he would do nothing.

Then when he was twenty years old he realized he must act, and act quickly. His aunt and uncle were making plans for him to study for the priesthood, and it was impossible to explain to them how he felt. They were faithful Catholics and would never understand how their own nephew, whom they had raised, could want to become a Protestant. So Joseph Rieger ran away. For a year he hid in Switzerland, earning his living by working for a man who was a weaver.

When he was twenty-one, he left the Catholic Church and entered the Mission House at Basel, Switzerland, where he spent four years preparing to be a Protestant minister.

Then Joseph Rieger made the second great decision of his life—to go to America to work with German-speaking people on the frontier.

Life on the American frontier in 1836, when Joseph Rieger was ready to begin his ministry, was rough and dangerous. St. Louis was a city of eleven thousand people on the edge of a wilderness. The country to the north and west was populated with small settlements separated by forests and almost impassable trails. There were few comforts, few doctors, few churches and ministers. But there were people who were struggling to cultivate the land and earn a living. Many of these people were from Germany. They had come to the United States with hope and courage. They were willing to work hard, but they were often lonely and afraid. Rieger felt called to serve these people.

It took Joseph Rieger six weeks to cross the Atlantic Ocean in a sailing ship. The voyage was rough and unpleasant. He and the other passengers were crowded together in small quarters, and food and water were scarce. New York City was a welcome sight when the ship finally anchored and the passengers could go ashore.

From New York, Joseph Rieger went to Hartford, Connecticut, where he lived for three months, practicing English and becoming acquainted with American life. He asked all the questions he could think of about the country to the west that would soon be his home.

At last, in September of 1836, he and another minister started westward. Each had one hundred dollars for his travel and living expenses. It took many days to cover the country by stagecoach, on horseback, and even at times on foot. Joseph Rieger was very tired when he finally settled down in Alton, Illinois, to begin his work.

His first home was a small room heated by a temperamental wood stove for which he was expected to chop the wood. The stove worked fairly well when the wind blew from the right direction. When it did not, the room was almost unbearably cold.

But a cold house was not Joseph Rieger's greatest problem. What was more discouraging was the response of the people. In his diary for January 29, 1837, he reported that in spite of beautiful weather only one man appeared for the church service.

Disaster and Escape

Seven months later Joseph Rieger decided to leave Alton. He preached his farewell sermon to five persons and went to Beardstown, Illinois. For a year he worked and preached there and felt that he was accomplishing something worthwhile. Then disaster struck the town in the form of an epidemic of typhoid fever. Many people became ill and died. Rieger visited the sick and helped in every way he could. He was nurse, doctor, friend, and minister.

But one day he was not seen in the homes or on the streets. Another day passed, and still no one saw him. A few wondered what had happened, but they were so busy with their own troubles that they did not bother to find out where he was. One small boy, however, decided to go to Rieger's home. He pounded on the door, but there was no answer. The boy tried again. This time when no response came, he went in. There he found Joseph Rieger lying on his bed, unconscious with fever.

For two days it seemed certain that Rieger would not recover. But slowly his health returned, and he was able to preach and work again.

The next year he went to Germany for a visit and married a young woman who returned to America with him. She was glad to be a minister's wife and looked forward to helping her husband in his church. But she soon discovered that being a minister's wife on the American frontier brought many hardships.

Part of the return trip westward to Illinois was made by stagecoach. At one point the coach had to cross a river with steep banks. The bridge across the river was not completed when the coach reached the crossing. The driver looked at the bridge, estimated its strength, and then asked the passengers to get out.

"You'll have to cross the bridge on foot," he said. "These planks won't hold the horses, the coach, and you too. I'll take the coach across first, and you follow. And mind you, walk carefully."

The passengers waited anxiously while the horses and coach crossed. Then the driver called back, "Better come one at a time. We may have weakened the supports!"

Mrs. Rieger watched with great interest as the men and women made their way over the bridge. Everything was new and exciting to her. While she was waiting her turn, she looked around and noticed some animals on the other side of the river.

"What are they?" she asked her husband.

Rieger looked in the direction she was pointing. "Those are oxen," he replied. "The men who are working on the bridge must have tied them to that beam."

When it was the Riegers' turn, Mrs. Rieger urged her husband to go first. "I'll start as soon as you're over," she promised. Joseph Rieger went across and waved to his wife from the other side. "Don't worry," he called. "The boards are steady."

Mrs. Rieger stepped carefully out over the water. The boards were firm, as her husband had said. But when she was almost across, something disturbed the oxen and they bolted, jerking the beam under her. She lost her balance, and unable to steady herself, she fell twenty feet into the cold water of the river.

Mr. Rieger rushed down the bank and pulled his wife out. To his great relief, she seemed unhurt except for a few scratches. But the shock of the experience and the unexpected ducking made it necessary for her to rest a few days before she and her husband continued the strenuous journey to their new home in Highland, Illinois.

The next two years were happy ones. Mrs. Rieger helped her husband, and the people in the congregation responded to his leadership. But he often wondered if what he preached about was important to the people. He wondered if they knew what it meant to be part of the church. He had no way of being sure.

The Church for People Who Did Not Want It

In 1841 a son was born to the Riegers. But when the baby was just three months old he became ill and died.

Two years later another son was born. When he was only seven months old Mrs. Rieger became seriously ill and died. Just six weeks after this Mr. Rieger's second son developed a very severe case of the measles, and because no one knew what to do for him, he too died.

Again Joseph Rieger was alone. During this difficult time he continued his work, hard as it was not to be overcome by his sorrow and loneliness. He was sure he was doing what God wanted him to do, and he found he had the courage and faith to do it.

As Rieger served the churches on the western frontier, he never knew from day to day what kind of task he would face next. Many people had little use for the church. If he were to serve them, he had to be ready to meet them under all kinds of circumstances and seize every opportunity to help them.

One evening a group of drunks decided that they would have some fun with the minister and repay him for his sermons against drunkenness. After much arguing and discussing among themselves, they planned to go to the Rieger home and break the windows.

Somewhat unsteadily the men started down the street, shouting and singing as they went. Some were so drunk they fell down and could not get up again. Others got cold feet and dropped out of the group. Only one man kept on. He was too drunk to realize he was alone. When he arrived at the Rieger home, he struck at the windows with a stick, sending the glass flying in many directions. Then he pounded on the door, shouting and ordering the preacher to come out and face him.

Mr. Rieger came to the door and opened it just in time to catch the drunken man as he fell, unconscious. With a great deal of effort Rieger pulled him into the house and put him to bed. His clothes were filthy. Mr. Rieger washed them and shined the man's shoes.

When the man awoke the next morning he did not know where he was or how he got there. Then, remembering the events of the night before, he struggled to get out of bed.

Mr. Rieger heard him stirring and came in. "Good morning," he greeted his surprised guest. "You're awake in time for coffee. Come and have breakfast."

The man looked at the minister, first in amazement, and then in great embarrassment. "Breakfast? Me? I'm not hungry. Just let me go home. I'll have your windows fixed, and I won't bother you again."

Mr. Rieger insisted that he stay, and as the man ate and talked with the minister he realized that he was really welcome.

Later that day the windows were repaired, and soon a new member was added to the rolls of Rieger's church, a member who became one of the most active workers in the church. "I've never met a person like Mr. Rieger," the man said many years later. "He wasn't angry. He wasn't afraid. He wasn't even upset. He took what happened as a good opportunity for us to become acquainted, and somehow I never wanted to get drunk again."

There were other occasions when drunken men threatened, abused, and swore at Rieger. Each time the minister tried to use the occasion to show the love and fellowship of the church. He wanted these men to find a more satisfying kind of life. Often he succeeded. Many times he failed, but he kept on trying.

Some of the attacks were not from drunkards but from people who thought the church was foolish. No person with any sense would belong to the church, they said.

One afternoon Joseph Rieger, on horseback, was on his way to a small community where he had agreed to preach. He came to a farm owned by one of the men who was against the church. The farmer was on the roof of his home, struggling with a lightning rod that he could not adjust. At the sound of the approaching horse, the farmer looked down and saw the minister. "I see you're on your way again, preacher," the farmer

called. "Why don't you stop your talking and do something useful?"

"What would you suggest?" Mr. Rieger asked.

"Something that's work—like fixing this lightning rod of mine," the farmer replied.

"Having trouble?"

"Well, yes," the farmer admitted.

"Let me take a look," Mr. Rieger replied. He dismounted and threw the reins over his horse's head. Then he climbed up the ladder and joined the farmer on the roof.

The farmer watched in surprise. Joseph Rieger looked at the rod carefully and made some suggestions. The farmer looked even more surprised. Together they set to work, and a few minutes later the rod was in place. The farmer scratched his head.

"Well," he commented. "I never would have guessed it. A preacher who can fix a lightning rod!" He paused uncertainly. "Want to have a bite to eat?" he asked.

Rieger smiled but shook his head. "No, thank you. I need to get on to my talking. But I appreciate the offer."

Mr. Rieger mounted his horse and waved good-bye. "Next time I'm along this way I'll try to stop. And I hope your lightning rod works."

New Tasks Bring New Skills

The years passed. Joseph Rieger married again and moved to other churches. This frontier minister was incapable of doing just enough to get by. He worked hard, and he let his imagination and his desire to serve God lead him into new activities.

In 1847 he went to a congregation near Holstein, Missouri. Here he helped to start a school to train ministers. As the west became settled, more and more men were needed to serve the churches. In order to be a minister a man needed to learn many things. Joseph Rieger tried to teach some men in his home, but this was not satisfactory. A real school had to be started.

A building was found in Marthasville, Missouri. In it the men would eat, sleep, attend classes, and study. Mr. Rieger looked over the building thoughtfully. There was no furniture, no kitchen equipment, and none of the materials a school ought to have.

One morning he made an announcement to the members of his church: "The students want to move in. They will find only an empty house with nothing in the kitchen or cellar. We, as neighbors, ought to do all we can to remedy that."

The church people responded with enthusiasm. The following day Mr. Rieger asked two of the prospective students to go out and collect the articles promised by the church members. As one student was about to leave, Mr. Rieger called him back and tied a rope around his waist.

"What's that for?" the student asked. "People will wonder about it."

"That is exactly what I hope they will do," Mr. Rieger replied. "When they ask, you say that I thought some one would like to give our new school a cow, for the students will need milk!"

That evening the young man returned, loaded with articles for the seminary house. Tied to the rope around his waist was a cow—and the cow was leading a calf!

When the Riegers left Holstein they went to Jefferson City, Missouri. Here Mr. Rieger visited the Missouri State Penitentiary. It was filled with prisoners who needed the church and the concern and friendship of church people.

He volunteered to be chaplain at the prison and to hold services every two weeks. Many of the prisoners came to know and love him. To them he was a man of God who brought God's love to them at a time when they especially needed it.

Joseph Rieger died in 1869. He was only fifty-eight years old, but the Catholic boy from Germany lived long enough to become known all over Illinois, Iowa, and Missouri. The title he might have had as a priest was given to him by the people he served, not because they had to, but because "Father Rieger" was the way they thought of him.

TORNADO IN TOWN

MARTIN LUTHER watched gravely as the procession of junior boys and girls walked down the center aisle of the church sanctuary toward the chancel. Leading the group were several juniors dressed in the robes of first-century Palestine. Behind them came more boys and girls wearing the clothing of many different times and places. There were the brown robes of monks, the dress of pioneers who had settled America, the colorful clothing of nations in which the Christian church had been established during the two thousand years of its history.

Mr. Loren, the minister, was at the end of the procession. In his hands he carried two books. One was the first pulpit Bible of the church. The other was a book that had come off the press less than two weeks before—*Fifty Years of First Church, Franklin.*

From her position near the organ, Miss Drake, a junior teacher, watched the slow movement of the procession. As the boys and girls approached Martin Luther they nodded their heads in greeting and then took their positions in the choir pews. Everything was going smoothly. Miss Drake was proud of her group. This pageant was their own idea. They had planned it as their contribution to the fiftieth anniversary celebration of their church, to be held on the coming Sunday afternoon.

Mr. Loren reached the chancel, greeted Martin Luther, and took his seat. This was the cue for the first-century Christians to dramatize their scene from the story of the church. They were just starting when Miss Drake felt an urgent tug on her arm.

"This is an emergency," she heard the custodian whisper, alarm in his voice. "I must talk to you."

Miss Drake turned to him in surprise, ready to protest, but one look at his face made her change her mind. She had never seen him so upset.

The two slipped out a side door. "Whatever is the matter?" she asked. "Has there been an accident?"

"No," he answered quickly. "I've had my radio on. There are tornado warnings. The storm is headed in our direction, and everyone is urged to get home as quickly as possible. Several towns have already been hit. There's no time to lose."

Miss Drake looked out the window. The sun had disappeared, and gray clouds covered the sky. She could tell that the wind was rising by the swaying of the trees.

"These children come from all over town. We can't send them out alone. I must talk to Mr. Loren." Miss Drake turned quickly to go back to the sanctuary.

"Their parents will be here," the custodian said. "The whole town will have the news by now."

He was right. In the few minutes she had been away, the rehearsal had stopped, and six adults were talking to the minister. More came through the rear doors as she hurried toward the group.

Mr. Loren saw her anxious face. "You know the news," he said. "There still seems to be time to get our group home before the storm strikes. I'll tell the children what's happening."

"Boys and girls," his voice was quiet but clear enough to be heard by everyone. "A bad storm is heading our way. Those of you whose parents are here are to go with them immediately. The rest of you will wait with Miss Drake until your parents come. The custodian and I will try to call them and tell them what is happening in case they haven't heard."

To Miss Drake's relief none of the boys and girls showed panic. Those whose parents had arrived left quickly. The others gathered around her, asking questions. As calmly as possible, she told about the tornado. "It may go completely over or around us," she added. "You never know how these storms will behave. We'll stay here for a few minutes so your parents can find you easily. Then, if the storm comes nearer, we'll go into the basement. This church is one of the strongest buildings in town."

Bob Lowe tugged at the brown robe he was wearing as Martin Luther and asked a question that had not occurred to Miss Drake. "But what about our pageant? Will the storm keep us from having it?"

Miss Drake looked at the boys and girls. The expressions on their faces told her how much the pageant meant to them.

"I don't know," she replied. "We'll have to see what happens. I hope we can have it. Everyone in the church has been working on the anniversary celebration. They'll want the whole program to be held unless it's really impossible."

Bob nodded, but Miss Drake knew he and the others were worried. "I'll tell you what," she added as an idea struck her. "Why don't we practice our songs while we're waiting?"

The children responded quickly, and for the next few minutes the sound of singing greeted surprised fathers and mothers as they hurried into the church.

"I didn't expect to hear 'A Mighty Fortress,' " Mr. Lowe declared when he came for Bob. "But I was glad to. Is there any one else we can take along?"

"I don't believe so, but thank you," Miss Drake answered as she looked at the few remaining boys and girls. "Mr. Loren is calling all the homes as quickly as he can. We'll stay here a few minutes longer and then go to the basement if we need to."

Mr. Loren and the custodian returned just as the last parent and child were leaving. "We still don't know whether Franklin will be in the path of the storm," he said. "But I'm glad all the children are on their way home. Now you'd better go too. We'll move the important church records into an inner office, and then we'll be on our way."

When Miss Drake stepped outside, she was glad she had only one block to go. The sky was dark, and sharp gusts of wind blew dirt and leaves into her face. Closing her eyes to a squint, she walked as quickly as she could toward her home and toward whatever the next few hours would bring.

A Big Decision

The tornado came to Franklin. Mr. Loren and his family in their basement, Miss Drake and her neighbors in an inside room of their apartment house, the juniors and their families in the safest places they could find, first heard hail. It rattled against the windows and pounded on the streets. Then a huge black column of churning wind ripped through the town, wrecking homes and buildings. It tore across the east side, leapt over the main business district, and touched down again in the open country.

The area over which the tornado jumped was undamaged except for a few broken windows. The area it hit was a shambles. Roofs were torn from homes, telephone poles were tossed across streets, and broken electric wires fell sputtering and twisting on lawns and sidewalks.

When the rain was over, Bob Lowe and his father opened their front door and looked around. There were few signs of damage.

Miss Drake and Mr. Loren met the same welcome sight. "Perhaps we escaped after all," Mr. Loren said to his wife. "Let's see if we can get any news on the radio or television. This is too good to believe."

What he learned sent him hurrying to the town hall where rescue work was being organized. Several hundred families were homeless. An unknown number of persons had been injured or killed. His was the only Protestant church building in town that had escaped serious damage. The storm was the worst disaster in the community's history.

For the next two days everyone who could help went to the aid of the tornado victims. Miss Drake called her juniors and asked them to bring clothing and food to the church. Other church school teachers did the

same. Doctors and nurses and those with first aid training worked without sleep caring for the injured.

Saturday noon Mr. Loren awoke after his first rest in forty-eight hours and remembered that the next day his church was celebrating its fiftieth anniversary. No announcement had gone out about any change in plans. He knew how much hard work many people had put into the services that had been arranged. He thought of the juniors and how eagerly they had been looking forward to presenting their pageant.

"Fifty-year anniversaries only come to a church once," he said to himself. But as he thought of this, he remembered what he had seen in the last two days. Four church buildings in the path of the storm were completely destroyed. The members of these congregations had no place to worship and no rooms for church school classes.

Mr. Loren lay quietly for a few minutes thinking. Then he went to the telephone. He called Miss Drake, he called the managers of the radio stations and the ministers of all the Protestant churches that had been destroyed, and he called the church officers.

Before he had hung up from his last conversation, many other telephones were in use. Miss Drake was busy talking to her co-teachers in the junior department, and soon they were talking to the boys and girls. Members of First Church were surprised to receive calls from chairmen of church committees. They were still more surprised to hear an announcement about their church on the radio. The message was always the same: "There will be an emergency meeting of all members and friends of First Church at seven-thirty this evening. Please try to come. The meeting is important."

Bob Lowe heard the news first on the radio. He hurried into the kitchen to tell his mother. A few minutes later his father had a telephone call urging his family to come. The receiver was barely back on the hook when Bob heard from Miss Drake.

"But what for?" he asked her.

"I don't know," came the reply. "Mr. Loren asked me to let you know he wanted us all to be there, that the meeting is very important. Will you come?"

"I think so," he answered. "Dad got called too. Do you suppose it's about our pageant?"

"It may be," Miss Drake answered. "I'll see you at the church, Bob. Good-bye."

"Well, what do you know!" Bob exclaimed to his mother. "Do you suppose we'll have our pageant? I sure hope so!"

By seven o'clock that evening the pews of First Church were filling rapidly. A number of people who came had been hurt by the tornado. To Bob Lowe's surprise three members of the junior department wore bandages. The homes of some others had been badly damaged.

"I didn't know any people from here had been hurt," Bob remarked to his father. "When the church was OK I just thought we all were."

"Many were not as lucky as we were, Bob," Mr. Lowe said. "That tornado destroyed a lot of property and hurt a lot of people."

"I guess it did. Do you suppose we can do something else to help?" Bob asked.

"Perhaps this is why Mr. Loren asked us to meet here tonight. He's coming in now. We'll soon know."

Mr. Loren waited quietly while the whispering in the congregation died away. "Friends," he said, "the last time I was in this chancel our juniors were rehearsing for our fiftieth anniversary celebration. They were singing a hymn that is appropriate for us now. Let us begin our meeting this evening by singing together 'A Mighty Fortress Is Our God.'"

When the last notes of the hymn had been sung and the people had settled in their seats, Mr. Loren spoke again. "I called you together this evening because I want to talk with you about a matter that concerns me very much. Tomorrow we celebrate the fiftieth anniversary of our church. Our plans are made. Our program is ready. What has happened to Franklin this week may lead us to feel that it is more important than ever to have our celebration. Perhaps we need to remind ourselves that nothing can destroy the spirit of our church.

"We are, however, very much aware of the damage the tornado did to other church buildings in our community. The members of these congregations have no place to worship tomorrow or on the Sundays that follow. These churches have many organizations that meet during the week just as we do.

"I have done some thinking. If we offer our building to these other churches for their use Sunday afternoon and evening and during the week, they can continue their work.

"The ministers would like to have services tomorrow. They feel that more than ever their people need to worship, to remember that God is able to help them meet the tragedy that has come to them. Many people have been hurt; a few have died. Homes were damaged and destroyed, and some people have lost everything they owned.

"If we offer our church building to them, it will mean that we can't have the big celebration we had planned for the afternoon and evening. Our morning service can take place, but all the other activities will need to be cancelled or postponed.

"I don't want to tell you what to do, nor do I think the adults should decide for the children and young people. I suggest that we meet separately for half an hour in order that the children may talk with their leaders and the young people may meet with their advisers."

Bob looked at his father in dismay. "This means we won't have our pageant! We can't after what Mr. Loren just said!"

"It isn't an easy decision," Mr. Lowe told his son, "but why don't you go and talk it over? Perhaps you'll feel that the pageant is too important to postpone. The big thing is to remember that we are a church. We need to think and act like one."

Bob nodded, but like other juniors, he was glum when he joined his teacher.

Miss Drake did not miss the expressions on the faces of the boys and girls, and she understood why they felt as they did.

"We have a decision to make," she said to the group as soon as everyone was seated. "It's an important decision because tomorrow is our fiftieth anniversary, and we have all looked forward to the services we have planned. Not only you but your mothers and fathers have worked hard on our pageant."

One of the juniors broke in. "That's right! They made the costumes and helped us get our props. They'll be disappointed if they don't have a chance to see the pageant."

Miss Drake nodded. "They will. But we have to think of the need other churches have for our building. What is the best thing to do?"

For a moment no one spoke, then several juniors talked at the same time. Miss Drake did not interrupt. She listened.

"Why can't we have our pageant and let the other churches use our building on Monday?"

"Why can't they meet in the schools? No one's there on Sunday."

"We worked awfully hard, and it's a *good* pageant!"

The conversation continued. Finally, Miss Drake broke in. "I gather that you feel we should go ahead with our plans."

Again there was silence. Then Bob spoke. "I *want* to have our pageant. But I don't know whether it's right to have it. Do you think it's right, Miss Drake?"

Some other children looked at Bob doubtfully. One or two nodded as though they were wondering about the same question.

"What do you mean, 'right,' Bob?"

"Well, I was just thinking, what if this church had been blown down by the tornado? I guess I'd like it if some other people said we could use their church."

"I would too," a few of the juniors agreed. "But why do we have to give up the church in the afternoon? Couldn't the others meet at night?"

"There are several different church groups that want to have services," Miss Drake reminded the group.

"But why can't they have one service and let each minister preach?" one boy asked.

"Maybe they could," the teacher responded. "But wouldn't that be a little like having one junior department with all the children in Franklin coming and each teacher giving a lesson?"

"I guess it isn't such a good idea," the boy agreed a little reluctantly.

"Miss Drake," Bob spoke again. "My father said the important thing is for us to act like a church. Does this mean we should let everyone use our building?"

"What do you think, Bob?" Miss Drake answered.

"I guess it does," he said slowly. "A church tries to help people, and we sure have a chance to help now. I guess I'll vote for giving up the pageant, but it sure isn't easy!"

"Bob has only one vote." Miss Drake turned to the others, "What do the rest of you think?"

"I guess we should," one after another decided. "I want our pageant, but it wouldn't be right to have it."

The vote was taken. Some of the hands weren't raised very high, but they all went up.

"I think we've acted like a church," Miss Drake said. "Now let's go and tell the others about our vote. Who will be our spokesman?"

The group all looked toward Bob. "He's Martin Luther," they said. "Let him tell."

Bob looked a little uncomfortable. "What'll I say?"

"What do you want Bob to report?" Miss Drake asked the group.

Several children spoke up.

"Tell them we wanted to give our pageant, but we wanted to help the other churches too."

"Yes, that's why we decided to give up the pageant."

"OK," Bob said when he was sure he had enough ideas to speak for the group.

When he joined his family, his father looked at him questioningly. Several others also looked as though they would like to know what the juniors had decided. But Mr. Loren didn't give the people a chance to talk among themselves. He stood up as soon as the boys and girls returned.

"We won't lose any time," he said. "I know some of you still have work to do and are anxious to go home. Let's hear first from the high school people who had planned an evening program."

The spokesman for the young people stood up. "We decided that we should postpone our celebration. We feel that our building ought to be used by anyone who needs it."

Mr. Loren nodded. "Now let's hear from our juniors. This is the group that has been working so hard on a pageant. Miss Drake, who is reporting for your group?"

"Bob Lowe," Miss Drake answered.

Bob rose and started to speak, but Mr. Loren stopped him. "Bob, I think we can hear you better if you come up here."

Somewhat reluctantly Bob walked to where Mr. Loren was standing. He felt a little frightened speaking in front of so many people, but he knew what he was going to say. "We talked it over," he said slowly and carefully. "We want to give our pageant. But we decided we should act like a church, and let the other people use our building, so we voted not to give the pageant."

Bob turned to go back to his seat, but Mr. Loren stopped him. "Wait a minute, Bob. We have something to say to the juniors, and we'd like them to hear it while you are still here. Mr. Keene, will you report what the rest of us decided?"

Mr. Keene smiled at Bob. "Do you think the juniors can be ready to present their pageant at the eleven o'clock service tomorrow morning?" he asked.

Bob was too surprised to say anything. He looked toward Miss Drake. She seemed as surprised as he was.

"I don't know," he stammered. "Ask Miss Drake."

Mr. Keene laughed. "I will," he responded. "Miss Drake, we know the juniors have planned a pageant that will help us remember what the church has stood for in the past and what it stands for now. We'd like to have this pageant for our anniversary service tomorrow morning. Do you think you can do it?"

Miss Drake stood up. "I'll ask the boys and girls," she replied. She looked around at the juniors seated in all parts of the room. "Will all those who want to give the pageant and who can be here at nine o'clock tomorrow to get ready, please raise your hands?"

Every hand went up.

"We'll be glad to have our pageant," she told Mr. Keene, "and we'll be ready."

Bob was very quiet on the way home after the meeting. Finally his father asked, "Something on your mind, Bob?"

"It's funny the way it turned out," Bob said. "We get to give our pageant, and the others get to use the church. I was thinking of how we would have felt if we had decided we wanted the pageant in the afternoon. I'm sure glad we didn't."

"What made you decide to give up the pageant?"

"Oh, we thought it wasn't right. We thought a church should help people."

Mr. Lowe agreed. "That's an important part of being a church. And, Bob, it might not have worked out the way it did. Things don't always go the way we want them to. The important thing is to do what we feel is right. Then, whatever happens, we know we've done the best we could."

Bob took a deep breath. "It was an exciting meeting, wasn't it? And I guess Miss Drake was as surprised as we were!"

The next morning an eager group of juniors checked their costumes and tried to remember exactly what they were to do. Then, as the first notes of "A Mighty Fortress Is Our God" came from the organ, Martin Luther again walked to the chancel and faced the procession of juniors as they marched slowly down the aisle of the church.

Miss Drake took her place near the organ. She noticed the serious expression on the face of every boy and girl and the quiet attention of the congregation.

The moment came when the first-century Christians went forward to act out the meaning of the church for them. This time there was no urgent tug on Miss Drake's arm, no alarming news. One scene followed an-

other as the children dramatized the response of people in all ages to Jesus Christ.

As the pageant came to an end, Mr. Loren rose and spoke to the congregation. "This morning we have worshiped together as the members of our junior department reminded us of the great story of the church. The church has come a long way and fought many battles. We have learned to stand for truth and justice, to help people, and to try to show God's love everywhere in the world.

"As we leave here, let's remember that we do not belong just to First Church, Franklin. We belong to the Christian church, of which Peter and Stephen and Paul and Martin Luther are also members. Let us close our anniversary service by praying together the prayer that belongs to all followers of Jesus Christ: 'Our Father, who art in heaven—.' "

After the service Mr. Loren came into the room where the juniors were taking off their costumes. To his surprise he found the group gathered around Miss Drake, talking earnestly. "What's going on here?" he asked.

"We just thought of something," one of the girls answered. "If the people in the other churches are going to have church school here, they'll need paper and scissors and things. We don't have enough, so we're planning a canvass."

"Just like a church canvass," another junior explained. "We're each going to ask the people in our block for supplies. Then we'll bring them to the church."

"That's a wonderful idea!" Mr. Loren declared. "In fact, I couldn't think of a better way to begin the next fifty years of our church's history."

"Say, that's right!" Bob Lowe exclaimed. "The next fifty years have begun! Come on, let's get moving!"

PRONOUNCING NAMES

DEMETRIUS OF ANTIOCH

Demetrius	de-mē′ tri-us
Nicholas	nik′ ō-las
Eunice	yū′ nis
Jason	jā′ sun
Barnabas	bar′ na-bus
Antioch	an′ ti-ok

CARL OF WITTENBERG

Schumann	shoo′ man
Wittenberg	vit′ en-berg

JOHN ELIOT, Apostle to the Indians

Waban	waw′ ban
Cockinoë	kok′ i-nō′ ē
Algonquin	al-gong′ kin

FRONTIER PREACHER

Rieger	rē′ ger